This Book belongs to Kione

D1642284

So Please Keep Out !!

CONTENTS

BRATZ™

ANNUAL 2006

£7.99

www.bratzpack.com
TM & © MGA Entertainment, Inc.
All Rights Reserved.

Pedigree®

Published by Pedigree Books Limited,
Beech Hill House, Walnut Gardens, Exeter, Devon, EX4 4DH.
Email: books@pedigreegroup.co.uk

©MGA

all about...

Cloe™

Cloe's so creative that her whole life has become a work of art, from designing fantastic fashions to creating cool new cosmetic looks to her tendency to be dramatic! Sometimes her imagination runs away with her, but her friends help this 'angel' stay grounded!

Nickname: Angel

Fave Colour: Turquoise

Lucky Number: 6

Fave Books: MYSTERIES (I TRY TO SOLVE THEM BEFORE THE END!)

Fave Movies: BIG EPICS

Fave Smoothie: BANANA

Fave Food: RIGHT NOW I'M VEGETARIAN...NEXT WEEK, WHO KNOWS!

Fave Music: IT CHANGES ALL THE TIME...THE HOTTEST NEW ARTISTS ON THE CUTTING EDGE!

Fave Class: ART

Fashion Passion: ANIMAL PRINTS AND SPARKLY FABRICS - DEFINITELY DRAMATIC!

Best Body Part: NECK

Shoppin' Style: BEAUTY PRODUCTS AND GLITTERING MAKE-UP

see page 37 for my travel tips!

©MGA

7

all about...

Yasmin ™

SOMETIMES YASMIN CAN BE A LITTLE QUIET, BUT EVEN WITHOUT HER SAYING A WORD, YOU CAN SENSE THIS GIRL'S SPECIAL. THERE'S JUST SOMETHING ABOUT HER THAT SEEMS ALMOST REGAL. BUT YASMIN'S NOT PRETENTIOUS! SHE'S REALLY OPEN-MINDED - SHE'S ALWAYS UP ON ALTERNATIVE TRENDS IN FASHION, FITNESS AND BEAUTY!

Nickname: PRETTY PRINCESS

Fave Colour: EARTHTONES (AUTUMN SHADES)

Lucky Number: 7

Fave Books: CHIC-LIT WITH HAPPY ENDINGS

Fave Movies: ROMANTIC COMEDIES

Fave Smoothie: APPLE

Fave Food: THAI, MEDITERRANEAN, ANYTHING ETHNIC!

Fave Music: FUNKY R&B WITH A GLOBAL BEAT, LIKE THE BLACK-EYED PEAS

Fave Class: CREATIVE WRITING

Fashion Passion: BLENDING DIFFERENT STYLES INTO A GRACEFUL GLAM LOOK

Best Body Part: HAIR

Shoppin' Style: BARGAIN HUNTER

See page 104 for my creative writing tips!

all about...

Phoebe

PHOEBE'S AS SWEET AS CAN BE, AND SO IS HER STYLE! THAT'S WHY ALL HER FRIENDS CALL HER 'SUGAR'! SHE'S ALWAYS CONCERNED ABOUT OTHER PEOPLE'S FEELINGS, WHICH IS WHY HER FRIENDS (AND HER TWIN SISTER, ROXXI™) COME TO HER FOR ADVICE!

Nickname: SUGAR

Fave Colour: PINK

Lucky Number: 2

Fave Movies: ROMANCES

Fave Books: SELF-HELP BOOKS

Fave Food: ANYTHING CHOCOLATE

Fave Music: LOVE SONGS

Fave Class: SOCIAL STUDIES

Best Body Part: EYES

Fashion Passion: HEAVENLY HIP LOOKS IN SOFT, FLUFFY FABRICS

Shoppin' Style: OUT-OF-THE-WAY BOUTIQUES

ALL ABOUT... Nevra™

YOU NEVER HAVE TO WORRY ABOUT WHAT NEVRA THINKS. SHE'S A GIRL OF ACTION, AND SHE DOESN'T HAVE TIME TO BEAT AROUND THE BUSH, SO THIS 'QUEEN B' ALWAYS TELLS IT LIKE IT IS! AND SINCE NEVRA™ JUST CAN'T STAND STILL, SHE'S GREAT AT SPORTS AND MARTIAL ARTS!

Nickname: QUEEN B

Lucky Number: 9

Fave Books: PHOTO BOOKS

Fave Music: R&B

Best Body Part: LEGS

Shoppin' Style: A FEW REGULAR STORES THAT I GO TO ALL THE TIME

Fave Colour: YELLOW

Fave Movies: MARTIAL ARTS FILMS

Fave Food: PEANUT BUTTER AND HONEY SANDWICHES

Fashion Passion: CASUAL COOL LOOKS THAT ARE SWEET LIKE HONEY

Fave Class: GYM

11

©MGA

ALL ABOUT...

Jade ™

ALWAYS ON THE CUTTING EDGE OF COOL, JADE'S THE ULTIMATE FASHIONISTA! AFTER CHECKING OUT THE LATEST FASHION MAGS, THE TRENDIEST BOUTIQUES AND ALL THE THRIFT STORES, SHE ALWAYS MANAGES TO PUT TOGETHER LOOKS THAT ARE COMPLETELY UNIQUE AND JUST SCREAM 'KOOL KAT'!

Nickname: KOOL KAT

Fave Colour: GREEN

Lucky Number: 11

Fave Books: I PREFER FASHION MAGS

Fave Movies: STYLISH FOREIGN FILMS

Fave Smoothie: STRAWBERRY

Fave Food: SUSHI, BECAUSE IT LOOKS SO COOL ON A PLATE!

Fave Music: GIRL POWER POPSTARS, LIKE GWEN STEFANI

Fave Class: CHEMISTRY, BECAUSE I LIKE MIXING ELEMENTS TOGETHER!

Fashion Passion: ANYTHING NEW AND QUIRKY-COOL

Best Body Part: LIPS

Shoppin' Style: THE COOLEST SHOPS AND THE HIPPEST STYLES

see page 86 for my sporty tips!

all about...

Sasha ™

Sasha's not afraid of confrontation - she knows who she is, what she wants, and how to get it! Fashion's a huge part of her life, but music is even more important to 'Bunny Boo!' Someday you can be sure she'll be a record producer...with her own fashion line!

Nickname: BUNNY BOO

Fave Colour: RED-VIOLET

Lucky Number: 3

Fave Books: BIOGRAPHIES OF SUCCESSFUL PEOPLE

Fave Movies: EDGY COMEDIES

Fave Smoothie: BLUEBERRY

Fave Food: POWER BARS

Fave Music: HIP-HOP, LIKE BEYONCE & JLO

Fave Class: DANCE (WHAT ELSE?)

Fashion Passion: MY STYLE COMES FROM THE STREET - OLD SCHOOL AND NEW FUNK

Best Body Part: HANDS

Shoppin' Style: LOOKIN' OUT FOR STYLES TO SUIT ALL MY FRIENDS

See page 52 for my concert tips!

15

Roxxi

Roxxi loves to spice it up! That's why her twin calls her 'spice'. Always ready for an adventure, she loves to try new things, and bring her friends along with her! When she gets an idea, she just goes for it!

Nickname: SPICE

Fave Colour: FIRE ENGINE RED

Lucky Number: 22

Fave Books: THRILLERS

Fave Movies: ACTION/ADVENTURE

Fave Smoothie: RASPBERRY

Fave Food: BIG JUICY HAMBURGERS (SORRY, CLOE!) AND FRIES

Fave Music: PUNK ROCK, LIKE AVRIL LAVIGNE & GREEN DAY

Fave Class: MUSIC (OF COURSE!)

Fashion Passion: RED-HOT ROCKIN' STYLES, ESPECIALLY DENIM AND LEATHER

Best Body Part: MY BIG MOUTH!

Shoppin' Style: WHEN I SEE SOMETHING I LIKE, I GET IT!

17

all about... Kumi™

KUMI'S FROM TOKYO BUT SHE WON'T STOP UNTIL SHE'S SEEN THE WORLD! HER FRIENDS THINK THIS WORLD TRAVELLER IS ONE "LUCKY BUG"! AND BECAUSE SHE WANTS TO CAPTURE THE MEMORIES, THE BEAUTY, AND THE GREAT NEW FASHION IDEAS SHE SEES EVERYWHERE SHE GOES, KUMI IS NEVER WITHOUT HER CAMERA!

Nickname: LUCKY BUG

Fave Colour: GOLD

Lucky Number: 12

Fave Movies: HORROR

Fave Books: CLASSIC NOVELS

Fave Music: TECHNO JAZZ

Fave Food: GREEN TEA ICE-CREAM

Fave Class: PHOTOGRAPHY

Fashion Passion: MIXING CLASSIC WITH THE CUTTING EDGE

Best Body Part: SHOULDERS

Shoppin' Style: IT'S ALL ABOUT GETTIN' JUST THE RIGHT ACCESSORIES!

18

©MGA

ALL ABOUT...

Dana™

DANA'S LOVE FOR SPACE AND SCIENCE INFLUENCES HER OWN, TOTALLY MOD STYLE! BUT IT'S HER COLLECTION OF FANCY FOOTWEAR THAT EARNED HER THE NICKNAME 'SUGAR SHOES!' DANA'S SUPER-SMART - YOU'LL ALMOST ALWAYS FIND HER EITHER READING OR ON THE COMPUTER. AND SHE WANTS TO OPEN THE FIRST SHOE SHOP IN SPACE!

Nickname: SUGAR SHOES

Lucky Number: 26

Fave Movies: SCI-FI

Fave Colour: PURPLE

Fave Food: CHOCOLATE CHIP COOKIES

Fave Books: BOOKS ABOUT SPACE, WHETHER IT'S FICTION OR NON-FICTION

Best Body Part: EYELASHES (AROUND PALE VIOLET EYES)

Fave Music: CLASSIC BLUES

Fashion Passion: TOTALLY SLEEK AND MOD OUTFITS IN SIZZLIN' SWEET COLOURS

Shoppin' Style: SHOES, SHOES AND MORE SHOES!

Fave Class: COMPUTER SCIENCE

Happenin' Holiday

WHAT KIND OF HOLIDAY WOULD SUIT YOUR STYLE BEST? DO THIS QUIZ TO FIND OUT!

The first thing I unpack on holiday is ...
a) my suntan lotion and sunnies.
b) my credit cards and shopping guide.
c) my camera (to snap all the amazing places I'm gonna visit).

My perfect day is ...
a) lazing around the house listening to music and reading fashion mags with my friends.
b) a major shopping spree in the city followed by a meal in an exclusive restaurant.
c) totally unplanned – just seeing what happens and having adventures!

My fave way to relax is ...
a) a bubble bath with scented candles and aromatherapy oils.
b) a trip to the smoothie bar followed by a facial and makeover in the beauty salon.
c) a friendly game of my fave sport, followed by a revitalising shower.

My wardrobe is mostly full of ...
a) bikinis and sarongs – I'm a sun worshipper!
b) killer heels, knee length boots and the latest chic accessories.
c) combats and t-shirts.

I couldn't live without ...
a) sunshine!
b) the mall!
c) my passport!

My idea of risk-taking is ...
a) booking a hotel without a swimming pool.
b) blending spots with stripes.
c) a solo parachute jump.

My favourite way to see the ocean is ...
a) from a sun lounger, watching the surfers ride the waves!
b) from the deck of a huge yacht.
c) diving to the coral reefs and swimming with dolphins.

I'm most likely to be crushin' on ...
a) someone laid back and chilled out.
b) the best-dressed lad in school, naturally.
c) the captain of the football team.

Answers

Mostly A's - Sizzlin'! You're a real sun goddess! You're never happier than when you're lying on a beach in a stylin' bikini. You should grab a flight to the tropics, seeking white sand, blue sea and palm trees!

Mostly B's - You're one hip chick. You'd be in your element on the stylin' streets of New York! Pack your lip gloss and your heels, and head for the bright city lights!

Mostly C's - Whether you're bungee jumping, white water rafting or trekking through the jungle, you love unexpected adventure and excitement! You should grab your rucksack and your passport, and go where the wind blows you!

I ♥ NY

Hi, I'm *Cloe* and I'm gonna tell you how a weekend away turned us into a kickin' crime-bustin' team!

I was just jetting out of the door on my way to pick up the girls in my scorchin' silver-blue Cadillac, when the postman arrived with a long thin white envelope, addressed to me.

Dear Cloe,
Congratulations! You are the lucky winner of Heavenly Hair's New York competition! You and three of your best friends have won an all-expenses-paid weekend in New York, including two nights in a luxury hotel and a fantastic shopping spree!
Best wishes
Heavenly Hair Shampoo Company

I squealed out loud – I could hardly believe it! I had entered the competition months ago and had totally forgotten about it! But there was no doubt who I'd be taking with me – I started the car and sped off to find my best gals!

©MGA

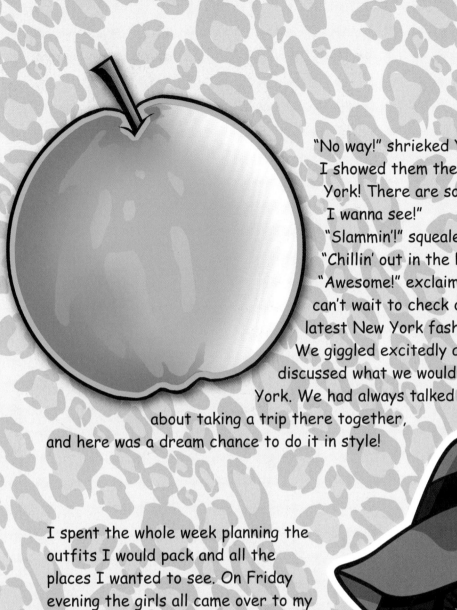

"No way!" shrieked Yasmin when I showed them the letter. "New York! There are so many places I wanna see!"

"Slammin'!" squealed Sasha. "Chillin' out in the big apple!"

"Awesome!" exclaimed Jade. "I can't wait to check out the latest New York fashions!" We giggled excitedly as we discussed what we would do in New York. We had always talked about taking a trip there together, and here was a dream chance to do it in style!

I spent the whole week planning the outfits I would pack and all the places I wanted to see. On Friday evening the girls all came over to my house with their weekend roller cases. We piled into the Cadillac and set off for the airport. I pumped up the stereo volume and we sang at the tops of our voices with the hood down!

We arrived at the airport, checked in and then went for smoothies in the airport lounge. "This weekend is gonna be awesome," said Jade happily, as she sipped the last few drops of her strawberry and vanilla smoothie. "I can't wait to see the shops on Fifth Avenue!"

"The art in the Met," I sighed.

"I've been reading about an amazing café in the Village," Yasmin said. "Loads of famous writers and musicians used to hang out there. It's got an awesome creative vibe."

"I'm just looking forward to some serious chillin' out time," Sasha added.

"Would passengers for flight NY100 please come to gate number three for boarding," announced the tannoy. We all jumped to our feet and raced through the lounge to gate three. We were first on the plane and we bagged four seats together in the middle.

As the plane took off we all linked hands and grinned at each other. "New York here we come!" I yelled. Jade pulled out a pile of the latest fashion mags, Yasmin began scribbling in her notebook and Sasha plugged us all in to her MP3 player and cranked up some hot hip-hop beats. I was too excited to do anything except imagine all the fun we were gonna have!

When the plane landed in New York,
we hopped into a taxi and cruised to our hotel. We were met by a
doorman in a red uniform with gold braiding, who smiled at us as
we stepped into the lobby. It was like a film set!

"Spectacular!!" I gasped, gazing at the marble floor and
luxurious décor.

"Totally rockin'," agreed Yasmin. We went over
to the check-in desk and got our room keys.
Sasha and Jade were sharing room 109
and I was in room 110 with Yasmin. Two
porters took our bags and led us up to
our rooms.

"This is so stylin'!" Jade raved,
walking around her room. The beds
had thick gold covers and the tall
French windows led out onto a balcony
that was shared between our two
rooms. The curtains were a warm
cream colour, held back with gold
tassels. Sasha flopped back onto her
bed and spread her arms out wide.
"Now this *is* luxury!" she declared.
We hooked a late-night snack in the restaurant
downstairs, then headed for our beds – we had a
busy weekend ahead and needed to get our beauty
rest!

The next morning I jumped out of bed and threw open the French windows. Sasha was already on the balcony, checking out the view.

"Hey girl," I said. "Time for action – we've got a lot to see!"

Sasha turned around and grinned at me.

"I've been ready for ages, *Angel* – Jade's just doing her makeup. So you guys better hurry up!"

I ran back into the room and found that Yasmin had already bagged the shower. "Don't be too long, *Pretty Princess*!" I called, as I chose my outfit for the day.

As soon as I had showered I stepped into my flares and plaid trench coat and slicked some clear gloss onto my lips. Yasmin looked fresh in her mini skirt and crisp white shirt.

Charlie, the doorman, grinned when he saw us.

"Cab, ladies?" he enquired. When we nodded he put two fingers in his mouth and gave a piercing whistle. A yellow taxi screeched to a halt next to us and we climbed in.

"Have a good day!" called Charlie as we jetted off, piled into the back of the cab! We waved goodbye and settled back, all grinning widely.

"Where to?" asked the driver.

"Fifth Avenue!" we chorused.

luscious lip gloss

TAXI

Girls on the town

©MGA

The taxi took us through Times Square on the way to Fifth Avenue and we cheered as we saw the flickering neon lights.

"I have *always* wanted to see Times Square!" whooped Sasha. We stepped out of the cab on Fifth Avenue and headed for the nearest boutique.

We spent half the morning jetting up and down the street, checking out the cutting-edge window displays and trying out all the latest looks. Finally, our bags bulging with fabulous new threads, we headed for the Empire State Building. I had seen a really romantic old film about two people meeting on the top, so we went right up and had our pics taken by the lift guard. Then we dropped our bags off at the hotel and went to a nearby café for some refreshment.

"Fifth Avenue was a blast," I gushed. "I'm really glad we did it. Now, what's the quickest way to the Met? Shall we splurge on another taxi or hop on the subway?"

The other three looked at me in surprise and all answered at once.

"But I thought we were going back to the shops!" wailed Jade.

"I want to hire blades and skate around Central Park," moaned Sasha.

"What about my writers' café in the Village?" complained Yasmin. "My favourite author wrote her first novel at one of the tables there!"

©MGA

"But, you guys..." I stammered, "...being able to visit the Met was the whole reason I entered the competition in the first place!"

"But there are so many shops I didn't get chance to check out this morning!" grumbled Jade. "How am I supposed to stay fashion-forward if I can't visit the hottest boutiques the one time I'm in style central - New York City?"

"I don't wanna go back to Fifth Avenue," said Sasha flatly. "It's supposed to be a relaxing weekend, right? Let's chill out a bit!"

"I'm *not* going roller blading," said Yasmin, looking upset. "I really want to go to the Village and see the writers' café. It's a really creative, inspiring place – you guys would love it!"

I suddenly lost my temper – I was feeling really upset that my best friends didn't seem to care about making the most of our weekend.

"I'm not going shopping, blading or sitting in some boring little café!" I yelled. "We can do all of that stuff back home, but we can't see this art anywhere except the Met! Don't be so selfish! You wouldn't even *be* here if it weren't for me!"

The other three glared back at me crossly.

"Well you can *go* to the stupid Met," snapped Sasha, jumping to her feet. "I'm here to relax and kick back, and that's exactly what I'm gonna do!"

She stormed out of the café as Jade and Yasmin pushed back their chairs at exactly the same time.

"Well if she's gonna please herself, so am I," Jade announced. "You two can do what you like."

She strolled out of the café. I could tell that underneath her cool attitude she was really upset as well, but I was too hurt and angry to care. Yasmin was hesitating by her chair.

"Go to your stupid café then," I snapped at her. "Don't let a little thing like being best friends stop you."

"Oh, if you're gonna be like that," she said, whirling around and leaving. I sat back in my chair, feeling totally wiped out. How had that happened? We were having a slammin' time five minutes before! I blinked tears out of my eyes crossly. If they were going to be selfish, then so was I.

I grabbed my backpack and pulled out my city map, then headed for the subway.

By the time I got to the Met I had stopped being angry and was just low. When I looked up at the building, I tried to feel the excitement I had felt earlier, but the argument had blown it away. I walked into the famous gallery and decided to go into the souvenir shop first, to try to get my buzz back.

Sasha was halfway to Central Park before she got over her temper and started to think about what had happened. She began to feel guilty. "Cloe was right," she thought. "She invited us to New York, and I just threw it right back in her face." Sasha stopped in the middle of the street, causing a total pedestrian jam. "I've got to apologise!" she said out loud. "And I *hate* apologising!"

Jade got to Fifth Avenue and was about to walk into a shoe shop when she saw a boutique we had all been in earlier. She glanced inside and saw another group of friends, laughing together. "It's not nearly so much fun on your own," she thought. "Time's a wastin'!" She turned around and hailed a cab.

Yasmin had marched back to the hotel room in a temper. But as she was seething, she saw the Polaroid we had taken earlier that day at the top of the Empire State Building. It's a great snap of us all! "What's the point in being here if we're not together?" she sighed.

Best Friends

©MGA

Meanwhile, I was browsing around the souvenir shop and trying not to think about what my best friends were doing without me. Suddenly I noticed that the guy in front of me was acting really weirdly. He was glancing around him, darting looks from side to side. Suddenly he pulled a bundle of reproduction print posters from the shelf in front of him, rolled them into a tube and shoved them under his coat! I was so shocked that for a minute I couldn't say anything, and he started to walk quickly towards the door. Then I found my voice.

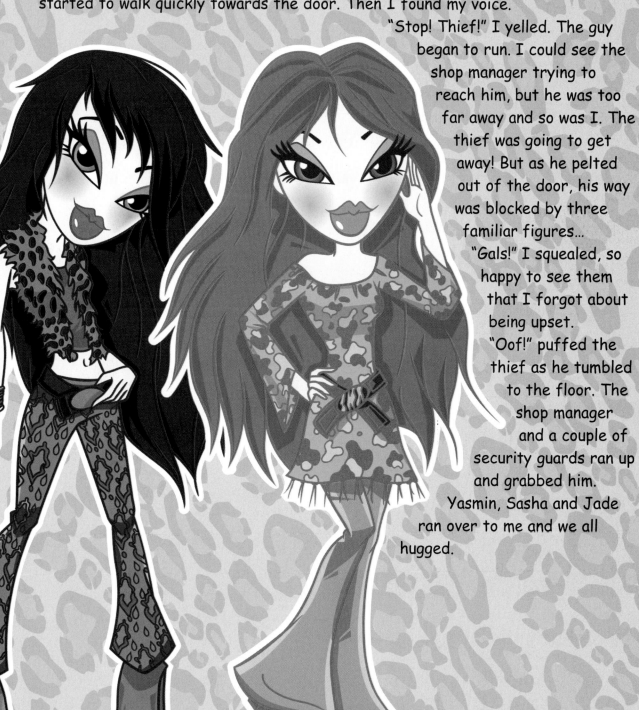

"Stop! Thief!" I yelled. The guy began to run. I could see the shop manager trying to reach him, but he was too far away and so was I. The thief was going to get away! But as he pelted out of the door, his way was blocked by three familiar figures...

"Gals!" I squealed, so happy to see them that I forgot about being upset.

"Oof!" puffed the thief as he tumbled to the floor. The shop manager and a couple of security guards ran up and grabbed him.

Yasmin, Sasha and Jade ran over to me and we all hugged.

"I'm sorry I was so mean!" burst out Sasha.

"I'm sorry too," chorused Jade and Yasmin at the same time.

"No, it's me who should be sorry!" I exclaimed. "I should have taken the time to find out what *everyone* wanted to do!"

Before anyone could reply, the shop manager came up to us with the stolen posters in his arms and a big smile on his face.

"Thank you, ladies, you just saved us a lot of money!" he said. "That was excellent teamwork!"

"Thanks!" I beamed, linking arms with my gals. "Best friends make the best teams!"

"Well now you can tell everyone that you foiled an art thief at the Met!" he joked. "As a reward, I'd like you to have these free entrance tickets, plus exclusive entry into a restricted area of the museum, where you can see some very special artwork."

"Thanks!" I gasped, taking the tickets. "Oh..." I turned to the others. "You guys don't have to come if you don't want to..."

"Of course we're coming," announced Sasha, back to her old bossy self! "Look, how about we spend the rest of the afternoon looking around the Met, then tomorrow do the other things we all want to do?"

We all agreed and headed for the museum entrance.

The Metropolitan Museum of Art
1000 Fifth Avenue, New York.

FREE ADMISSION
Admit:1

Full access to restricted area

The Metropolitan
Museum of Art

FREE ADMISSION
Admit:1

Full access

We had an awesome time looking around the Met – I was totally inspired by the off-the-hook art that we saw. The use of colour gave Jade some fabulous ideas for new fashion combos and Sasha and Yasmin both loved the sculptures. By the time we were ready to leave it was dark and we suddenly realised how hungry we were!

"How about we jet back to the hotel and change into our new gear, then hit the restaurant for a luxury-style meal?" suggested Jade.

"Good plan!" we yelled, and grabbed a taxi. Back at the hotel we all piled into Jade and Sasha's room and unpacked our boutique bags. I chose a strappy little black dress. Yasmin looked truly like a pretty princess in her tasselled dress and knee-length boots. Jade rocked in an emerald-green dress that matched her eyes and Sasha looked cool and stylin' in three-quarter length jeans and a sparkly top.

We went down to the restaurant and the waiter seated us at a round table. We ordered loads of food to share and some fizzy flavoured spring water.

"Here's to foiling the art thief!" I grinned, raising my glass.

"And to the gorgeous Met!" said Jade with a wink.

"To the bright city lights of New York!" added Sasha.

"I've got the best one," said Yasmin. "Here's to BEING FRIENDS!" We all cheered that one!

Cloe's Guide to

we were knocked out by the super-stylin' New York look! so we've picked out a few ways to get that chic streak!

Fashion - Start as you mean to go on! Prepare for your indulgent city look with a perfumed bubble bath, divine-scented soaps, aromatherapy oils and silky pajamas.

Be sure of yourself! If you've got bags of confidence, whatever you wear will have everyone else rushing out to copy you!

Know what suits you and don't be a fashion victim!

Take your time and pay attention to the details. The effort is always worth it.

Accessories - Chic sunnies are a must! Bags should be tiny and hand-held.

Forget silver jewellery – the luxury look is 100% gold! Choose delicate gold studs or a thin gold bracelet to give your look the finishing touch.

luscious
lip gloss

Makeup - Keep it simple and elegant, with a light brush of lip gloss and a delicate dusting of blush.

Big Apple Flair

Hair - Tie back your locks in a stylin' chignon – the latest New York look is simple and elegant. Get your friends to come over so you can try it out on each other. Don't worry about making the chignon too tidy at first — practise the method first, then improve on the neatness!

Party Time - Now you've mastered the New York look, why not throw a themed party for all your friends?

Invitations - Send invitations on postcards of famous New York landmarks!

Nails - Ask an artistic friend to paint tiny New York symbols on your nails!

Bargain Hunter - New Yorkers love a great bargain! Why not ask your gals to bring along any clothes or accessories they don't want any more, and see if you can mix n' match some brand new party looks!

Colour Scheme - Think red, white and blue, with stars and stripes, to decorate your party!

Drink - Invent some new smoothies and fruit drinks especially for the party!

Films - Rent a couple of old-style romantic New York films from the video shop and get out the hankies for those tear-jerkers!

Our Sizzlin' New York Snaps

Cloe and Yasmin

We had a slammin' time trying out the chic New York fashions!

Jade and Sasha

We looked stylin' when we stepped out in our new buys!

Jade and Cloe

Our scorchin' shopping outfits!

Cloe's Travel Tips

I LOVE TRAVELLING AND SEEING NEW PLACES! HERE'S MY GUIDE TO JETTING OFF IN STYLE.

Bag It - First you need a stylish suitcase to fill. No rucksacks, ladies! Pick a case with a drag handle and wheels. You don't want to carry anything heavier than your handbag!

Fashion Walk - Make a list of the clothes you'll need, depending on where you're headed.

For the beach you'll need some stylin' bikinis and chiffon sarongs.

For the city, pack some kickin', smart outfits and chic scarves.

Pack light – think mix n' match – and take plenty of lightweight accessories to give outfits a new look.

Smooth Skin - Take plenty of moisturiser and sun lotion, plus your fave lip gloss, eyeshadow and eyeliner. Keep your holiday look simple and quick.

Hot Hair - Pack a really good shampoo and conditioner to keep your locks luscious in the heat of the sun. Pack your hair straighteners for a fast-change evening look.

Happy Feet - Whether you're heading for a sandy beach or the streets of gold, you're gonna need some stylin' footwear.

Pack a pair of shoes for the daytime, a pair in a neutral shade for the evening and some loose sandals or trainers.

One Last Thing... - Don't forget to send me a postcard!

cloe x

Sun Block 15

ROCKIN' THE RUNWAY

Hi, I'm Nevra, and I'm gonna tell you how my best friends and I turned a fashion disaster into a fashion triumph!

It was midsummer and we were all lying on the grass in Jade's back garden, soakin' up the sun. Jade was reading a fashion mag. Sasha's face was half hidden by her stylin' Italian sunnies. You might have thought she was asleep except for her left foot moving to the beat of the hip-hop grooves on her MP3 player. Cloe was getting artistic, painting sunflowers on her toenails, and Yasmin was chewing on the end of her pencil and writing something in her notebook – so it was an average chilled-out Sunday afternoon. Yasmin sighed loudly and I looked up in surprise.

"What's crackin', Pretty Princess?"

"Oh, it's one of the charities I volunteer for," said Yasmin. "They've written to ask me for some fundraising ideas, but I just can't seem to get inspired."

"What charity is it?" asked Cloe.

"It raises money for orphans in poor countries," Yasmin explained. "It buys them food, medicine, clothes... but they haven't had many donations this year and they're worried that they won't have enough for all the children they take care of."

"Did you say *clothes*?" asked Jade, with interest. "Yasmin, I might be getting one of my brilliant ideas!"

"Always so modest!" teased Sasha, pulling her sunnies down her nose and looking at Jade over them. "What's your idea, *Kool Kat?*"

"How about we put on a fashion show?" Jade said simply.

"Oooh!" squealed Cloe in excitement. "Oh no! I've smudged the sunflower on my big toe!"

"Sorry, *Angel*!" Jade said with a laugh. "Seriously though, I bet we could raise loads of money for charity *and* have fun at the same time. Whaddya say?"

"I'm in!" declared Cloe.

"Me too!" agreed the rest of us. What could be more fun than combining friends and fashion?

Yasmin gave Jade a hug. "You're amazing!" she said. "Thanks for being such a great friend!"

We got down to planning the event straight away. Cloe took charge of photography, makeup and hair. Yasmin agreed to design the tickets and arrange the advertising. Sasha said that she would book the venue and plan the music, and Jade's job was to put together the clothes. I agreed to decorate the venue and find some models.

"What about a theme?" asked Sasha, sucking the end of her pen. Bunny Boo is never happier than when she's making lists and planning things!

"I think Jade should decide the theme," said Yasmin. "It's her idea that got us all started!"

"Well," said Jade decisively, "let's make it a Miami theme then. It's turning out to be a scorchin' summer and we can give the audience some fashion-forward pointers from the sunshine state! No one does the summer look better than Californians!"

The only free spot at the local hall was the following Saturday afternoon, which meant that we had very little time! But anything is possible when you all pull together. We had a totally manic week, trying to organise the show in time, but by Friday evening it seemed as though everything was going to be fine.

We met at Yasmin's house for a final run through and Sasha ticked off items on her long list of 'Things To Do' in her electronic personal organiser.

"Advertising and tickets?"

"I stuck posters up all around the school and across town," said Yasmin. "I've sold one hundred and fifty tickets – and there are loads more in case people just turn up on the day!"

Sasha made a big black tick on her list. "Jade, what about the clothes?"

"I've called every fashion boutique I could think of!" replied Jade. "Some of them wouldn't help – but I got two to say they would send us some of their most 'out there' samples – we can be a sort of fashion test for them!"

"Awesome!" I exclaimed. "If anyone knows how to use ahead-of-the-game fashions, it's you, Kool Kat!"

"They're sending all the clothes first thing tomorrow," added Jade. "I have to be at the hall early to meet the lorry. Is the venue all arranged, Bunny Boo?"

"Totally under control," said Sasha, flicking back her long silky hair. "And I've designed an awesome music scheme – I'll set it up this evening."

"I've booked a photographer," announced Cloe, "and my beauty kit is ready to rock!"

"What about the models?" Sasha asked me.

"Sorted," I told her. "My cousin is a model, and she is bringing a group of her modelling friends. I'm gonna decorate the hall tonight – I've designed some stylin' backdrops for the catwalk, all in the Miami theme, with palm trees and loads of colour."

©MGA

Sasha closed her organiser and flashed us a dazzling grin.

"So we have nothing to worry about!" she said. "See how easy things can be when you're organised? Now, how about a smoothie to celebrate?"

We linked arms and went to the smoothie bar.

Later that evening, Sasha and I headed for the hall to start setting up. While I worked on the décor, Sasha set up the music system and put her CDs in the right order. I worked really hard, decorating the hall, setting up the catwalk and rigging up a curtain for the models to prepare behind.

There was a little room at the back of the hall, which we set up as a dressing room for Cloe, and we prepared a space for all the fast clothing changes that were going to have to happen. It was really late when we finally left, but it felt great to know we had such a kickin' cool fashion show venue!

But next morning, things started to go spectacularly wrong...

The first problem came before I was even out of bed. My mobile rang and I flung out an arm to grab it and knocked over my bedside lamp.

"Whurr?" I mumbled into the phone, trying to wake up.

"You've gotta get down to the hall now!" squealed Yasmin down the line. I moved the phone away from my ear.

"What's wrong?"

"Jade just rang me – it's a disaster! The lorry carrying the clothes had an accident on the way here – the driver's ok but the clothes are ruined!"

"What?!" I sat up, wide awake in a moment. "You're kidding!"

"I wish I was!" wailed Yasmin. "What are we gonna do? Jade's being totally calm about it, but I know she's freakin' on the inside! The boutiques don't have any more samples to spare!"

"Oh no," I groaned, "what are we gonna do?"

"Just hurry down to the hall," said Yasmin. "We're all meeting there. Quick!"

Within fifteen minutes I was at the hall. Jade and Yasmin were already there – Yasmin looking frantic while Jade looked chilled. Before I could speak to them, my mobile rang again. It was my cousin.

"I've got bad news," she said. "I'm really sorry, but we can't make it this afternoon. Our agency has booked us in for a magazine photo shoot – there's just no way out of it."

"But you promised!" I exclaimed.

"I'm sorry," she said again, "but this is paid work – I can't turn it down for charity!"

©MGA

©MGA

I groaned after we said goodbye and told the others. "We've lost our models too," I sighed miserably.

"Oh well," shrugged Jade. "We've got no clothes for them to wear anyway."

"That's not all," said Cloe, who had just walked up behind us. "The photographer's ill – he can't make it."

"This is a nightmare!" Yasmin cried.

"Here's Sasha!" said Yasmin. She repeated the news about the models and the photographer. Sasha looked like thunder.

"Didn't you guys arrange any backup?" she snapped. I felt my temper start to bubble.

"In a *week*?" I retorted. "We did well to arrange anything at all!"

"So how come everything *I* organised is working just fine?" she enquired.

"Back off, Sasha," said Jade, raising an eyebrow. "We couldn't know any of those things would happen."

"Well, Nevra *could* have arranged for a few more models," said Cloe. I glared at her.

"*You* could have arranged for another photographer," I replied crossly.

"And why did Jade have to have all the clothes coming in the same lorry?"

"To save money!" snapped Yasmin. "In case you've forgotten, we're trying to raise money for charity here!"

Sasha glared at us and unlocked the hall. We all stepped inside. The other three gasped when they saw what we had done the night before.

"It looks fabulous," said Yasmin.

"Pity it was a total waste of time," Sasha snapped. She walked over to the stereo system and switched it on. "We needn't have bothered, Nevra. We're gonna have to cancel."

Before anyone could reply, there was a loud crackle and a bright flash. The amplifier made a strange whining sound and went dead. A little spiral of smoke curled out of the top of it.

Sasha stared at the amplifier and we stared at Sasha, waiting for her to explode. There was a long pause, then the corner of her mouth began to twitch.

"That'll teach me!" she said, turning to us and holding out her hands. "I'm sorry, you guys. I had no right to yell at you – I just lost my temper. We're in a real mess!"

We all grinned ruefully. But Jade had a familiar gleam in her green eyes. "You know what," she said, "we are being way too negative about this. We're best friends – we can do *anything*, right?"

We all started to feel a bit better.

"I've got an idea about the photographer!" said Cloe. "Why don't we ask Koby? He could borrow a camera from school and get some awesome shots for us."

"That's a scorchin' idea, *Angel!*" grinned Yasmin. "Koby's as good as a professional photographer – we should have just asked him in the first place!"

I was looking thoughtfully at the other girls. "You know," I said, "we don't need a bunch of professional models either. We all know how to wear fashion with flair! *We* can be the models! I'll give Dana and Meygan a call – I'm sure they'll help us out too."

"That's a crazy-cool idea!" whooped Jade. Then her face fell. "But having models is no help – we still don't have the clothes to put them in!"

"Jade, you are more fashion-forward than any of those boutiques!" exclaimed Sasha. "And you've got some of the hippest wardrobes in the country to choose from!"

"*Bunny Boo's* right," added Cloe. "You can take clothes from all our wardrobes and put together an ahead-of-the-game collection!"

"You're right!" Jade agreed. "But I'll need a hand – Yasmin, will you come with me?"

"Sure thing, *Kool Kat!*"

©MGA

Jade and Yasmin darted off to hit the fashion trail and Cloe, Sasha and I grinned at each other.

"Crisis over!" I said, heaving a sigh of relief.

"Not quite," sighed Cloe, pointing to the stereo. "We still don't have a music system."

"I just might have a solution to that," said Sasha with a wink. She pulled out her mobile and walked away to make a couple of calls. Cloe and I watched her with our fingers crossed.

"Sorted," she announced after the second call. "A couple of days ago I was chatting to Joe, the guy who owns the Jet Bar – you know the one that always has groovin' live music?"

We nodded, smiling. Sasha knows everyone who's anything to do with the music scene!

"Well, she continued, "Joe was telling me how he's accidentally double booked two bands for tonight, so he had to cancel one of them. I just rang to check if they're available this afternoon instead – and they said yes!"

Cloe and I squealed and threw our arms around Sasha.

"That is totally awesome!" I gasped.

"Live music is so much better than a stereo!" Cloe added.

©MGA

47

Next we rang Koby and explained the situation on speakerphone. He didn't sound too happy, and we could hear talking in the background.

"The thing is, ladies," Koby said, "all the guys are here and I had planned to go surfing with them."

We all groaned.

"But it's a *crisis*!" Cloe wailed.

"Look, why don't you *all* come?" interrupted Sasha. "There are enough cameras to go round – and if you're all together it'll be much more fun. And Koby, it's for a good cause! Whaddya say?"

Koby laughed. "Okay, okay! You're very persuasive, *Bunny Boo*!"

"We'll see you here at two thirty, then," Sasha declared, and hung up. Jade and Yasmin had a frantic morning, dashing around picking the best items from all our wardrobes and working out a fashion scheme. We rang everyone we could think of and begged them to be models for the afternoon! Dana and Meygan turned up, with our new friends Phoebe and Roxxi. Poor Cloe was rushed off her feet doing all their hair and makeup! Sasha took charge of organising the models and putting out all the outfits on racks for the quick changes.

©MGA

The band arrived and was setting up as Cloe started to do my hair. Koby strolled in with Dylan, Cameron and Cade. They were all carrying cameras.

"Ready for your close ups, ladies?" asked Cameron as he snapped a few scorchin' shots of Cloe.

"Ready as we'll ever be!" Yasmin replied. "Let's rock, girls!"

She threw open the doors, and saw there was already a long queue outside the hall!

Cloe

"Welcome to the Charity Fashion Show!" cried Yasmin. "Come on in!" The live band kicked in with some stormin' sounds as the audience packed into the little hall. All the tickets sold out! When we were sure everyone had arrived, we hit the spotlights, Jade grabbed the microphone to introduce the designs and the show began!

We had a blast struttin' our stuff on the catwalk and the fashion show was a major success. The crowd loved the décor and the live music, and Jade's last-minute Miami fashion line looked amazing! The boys were kickin' as photographers and we got plenty of stylin' snaps of the day. One of them even made it onto the front cover of the school magazine! But best of all was the awesome total we raised for Yasmin's charity – we proved that when it comes to fashion, nothing can hold us back!

Nevra

Yasmin

Spring Clean

IS YOUR WARDROBE A HAVEN OF HARMONY LIKE MINE OR A CRAZY CONFUSION LIKE JADE'S? FOLLOW THESE STEPS TO GET A CLOSET TO BE PROUD OF!

Storage
Space - Getting dressed should be fun, not frantic! Make sure your storage space works for you. You should have as many of these as possible:

Low hanging rail for trousers, skirts and shirts

High hanging rail for coats and dresses

Drawers with dividers for lingerie, socks and t-shirts

Open shelves for jumpers and hats

Storage boxes for shoes and accessories

A belt rack

A full-length mirror

Good lighting

©MGA

and Sort!

Contents - Crank up your fave tunes and take everything out of your wardrobe. It's time to clean up your fashion act! Remember, don't keep anything you don't look fabulous in!

Bin it! - Anything you have not worn for six months.
Clothes that don't fit you any more.
Old faves that have had their day!

Keep it! - Anything you love and wear all the time.
Clothes that can be jazzed up with a little fashion know-how!
Anything that has that retro vintage flavour!

Organise it! - Now you need a fashion plan. Organise your hanging rails according to venues – school, home, party, lazy weekend, concert – you'll never have to rummage to find the right outfit again!

Sasha's Concert Tips

WITH ALL MY CONTACTS IN THE MUSIC SCENE, I CAN ALWAYS GET EXCLUSIVE TICKETS TO THE HOTTEST CONCERTS FOR ME AND MY FRIENDS! WE'VE PICKED UP SOME GREAT TIPS TO MAKE THE MOST OF YOUR FAVE SHOWS.

Water - With all the dancing, singing and cheering you'll be doing, you'll need to rehydrate! Take a big plastic bottle of water with you to share around.

Autograph Book - If you get a backstage pass or meet your fave musicians, you'll need something stylin' to collect their autographs in! Make your own unique book using fabrics, glitter or cutouts from magazines.

Camera - We always take our cameras along to record our memories. Make sure you use a good zoom lens to get the best snaps.

Clothes - With our passion for fashion, we always look scorchin' when we step out! You'll need something strappy for while you're dancing, with a stylin' jacket for the end of the evening.

Hair and Makeup - Getting your look together is all part of the fun! Meet up with your friends to do your hair and makeup together before the concert.

Sasha x

Miami Smoothies

After we did our Miami Fashion Show, we got the smoothie bar to invent some off-the-hook taste sensations for us! Try out some of our faves! Just throw the ingredients in a blender, mix until they're super smooth and serve in long glasses!

Rockin' Raspberry

2 cups milk
1 cup fresh raspberries
6 teaspoons cocoa powder
2 teaspoons sugar

Apple and Blackberry Explosion

2 apples, peeled and chopped
2 cups blackberries
2 tablespoons vanilla ice cream

Kickin' Kiwi

2 Kiwi fruit peeled and chopped
1/2 cup orange juice
1 banana, peeled and chopped
1/2 cup vanilla ice cream
2 teaspoons sugar

Peach Passion

2 cups milk
1/4 cup orange juice
1 tin sliced peaches, drained
6 tablespoons vanilla ice cream

Stylin' Superstar

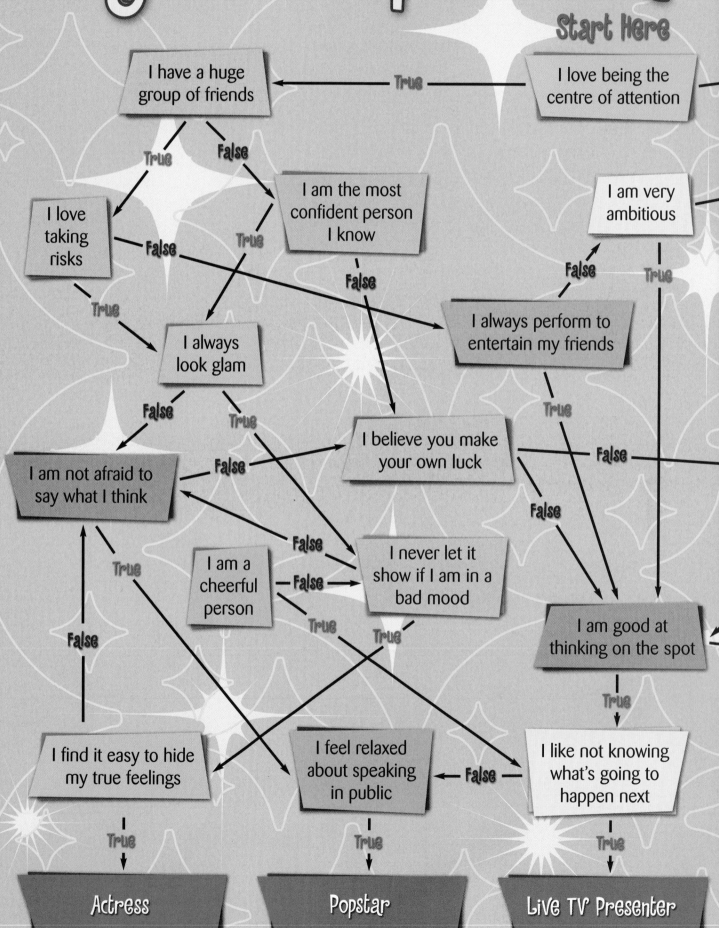

I love being the centre of attention

— True → I have a huge group of friends

I am very ambitious

I love taking risks

I am the most confident person I know

I always perform to entertain my friends

I always look glam

I believe you make your own luck

I am not afraid to say what I think

I am a cheerful person

I never let it show if I am in a bad mood

I am good at thinking on the spot

I find it easy to hide my true feelings

I feel relaxed about speaking in public

I like not knowing what's going to happen next

Actress

Popstar

Live TV Presenter

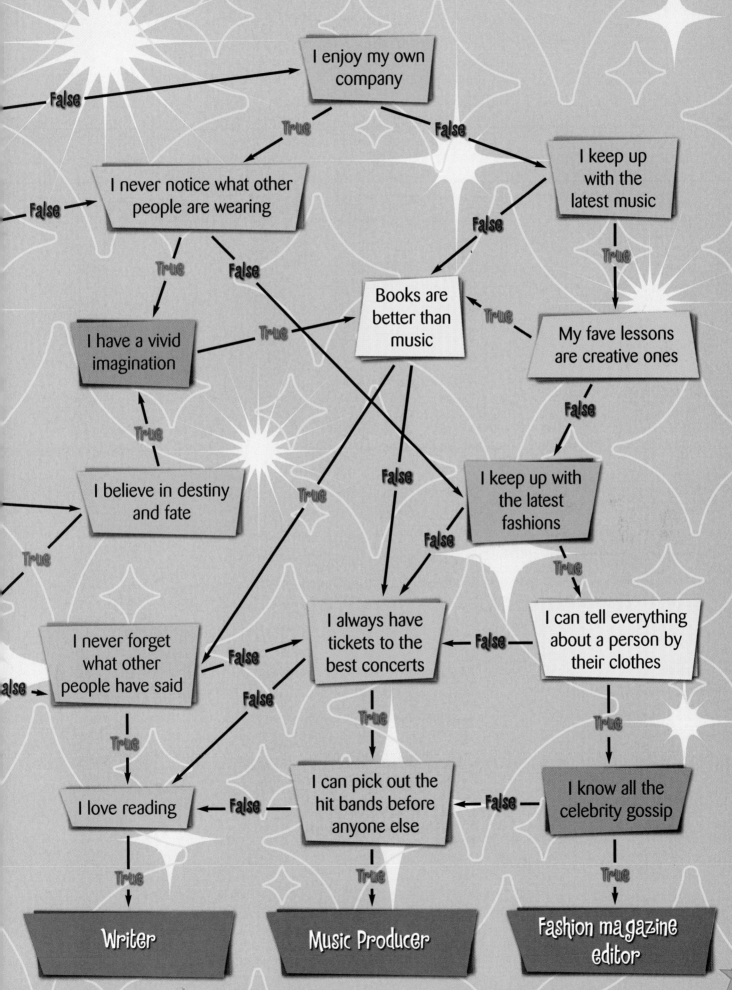

WE ALL KNOW YOU'RE GONNA BE FAMOUS SOMEDAY - BUT FAMOUS FOR WHAT?
ANSWER TRUE OR FALSE TO THESE QUESTIONS AND FOLLOW THE ARROWS TO FIND OUT!

ROCK ANGELS™

Hi, I'm *Jade*, and I'm gonna tell you about how one of the worst days of my life ended up landing me and my best buds as the stars of the world famous rock band, the Rock Angelz!

It all started when I met my best gals, Cloe, Sasha and Yasmin, at the mall, poring over *Your Thing* magazine.

"I got it! I got it!" I yelled.

"What'd you get? The latest Crash CD?" Cloe asked.

"Even better. I got the student work experience at *Your Thing* magazine!" I gushed. "I'm the new intern to Ms. Burdine Maxwell, editor-in-chief."

"That's awesome, *Kool Kat*," said Sasha. "That fashion-challenged magazine needs someone fashion-forward like you. Hold on there – Mean Girl Alert."

I looked to where Sasha was pointing and saw Kirstee and Kaycee, the two meanest girls at Stiles High. Everyone simply called them the Tweevils because they were twins who were seriously evil. They looked pretty much identical, except that Kaycee always had a bandage over her nose from one of her many nose jobs gone bad.

"Well look who's here," Kirstee said to me. "The fashion freaks."

I got really angry, but Yasmin helped me keep my cool.

The next morning, I arrived at the offices of *Your Thing* magazine feeling very excited. I had picked out a stylin' outfit and some hip accessories – I wanted to make a good first impression. Burdine was dressed all in pink with a tiara on her head, which seemed pretty un-fashion forward to me, but I didn't want to judge her. Apparently, it's because she sees herself as the reigning queen of fashion.

"Hi Ms Maxwell, I'm Jade, your new intern" I said. "I have a ton of ideas for the magazine and–"

"Stop!" she shouted. "Just so we understand each other, I come up with the ideas. Your title is ... nothing!"

I was crushed. But nothing could have prepared me for what came next. Kirstee and Kaycee walked in through the door.

"Ah, my other work experience students," Burdine sighed. "Two *lovely* girls. Right, I have all your tasks for the day."

She gave me a long list. Then she gave a single post-it note to Kirstee and Kaycee. "Now get busy," she said. Royale and I have some shopping to do." (Royale was Burdine's pesky little dog.)

"Neato, we got a fashion assignment!" Kaycee said. She began snapping shots of Kirstee. "That's gorgeous!" Kaycee said.

"Now, Jade, it's your turn."

Before I had a chance to pose, Kaycee took a picture of me, totally unprepared. "That will be perfect under the 'fashion don'ts' section!" she laughed.

fashion assignment

I looked at my list. I had to vacuum the rugs and curtains, water the plants, get all of Burdine's pink clothes dry cleaned, shine her shoes, organise her desk and get her lunch for the day.

"Hey guys," I said to Kirstee and Kaycee. "Do you think you could help me out? You've already finished your assignment and I have so much work."

"Sorry, fashion freak," Kaycee said, "NOP – that stands for Not Our Problem."

I was close to tears by that point, but I kept my cool. "Well, do you know what Burdine likes for lunch?"

"Sure," Kirstee said, "We'll phone in the order. You just have to pick it up."

I went to the deli and picked up Burdine's lunch – a gigantic hamburger. When I came back to the office, Burdine was looking at her post.

"Junk, junk and more junk!" she yelled, throwing all the letters to the floor. "Oh, just get me my lunch."

I gave Burdine her burger. She took one look at it and started hyperventilating.

"A burger? What are you trying to do, kill me? I only eat greens! Jade, you are fired. Get out!"

I was so bummed, I didn't know what to do. I began to think maybe I really was just one big 'fashion don't'. I went to see my best gals – Cloe, Yasmin and Sasha.

"Kool kat, you wouldn't have learned a thing at that lame magazine," Sasha said.

"You would be so much better than Burdine at running a magazine," Yasmin said.

"Pretty Princess, that's a slammin' idea!" Sasha exclaimed, looking around at us all. "Are you thinking what I'm thinking?"

"Yes!" we shouted. "Let's start our own magazine!"

Sasha found us a scorchin' office space and Cameron and Dylan helped us turn it into one of the most stylin' lofts downtown. But that wasn't even the best part. I was sorting through the letters that Burdine had thrown away, when I found something amazing!

"Guys, you aren't going to believe this," I said. "These are invitations to the exclusive opening of Pinz and tickets to the Save the Universe Benefit Concert in London! Every rock star in the world is going to be there! All expenses paid, accommodations included – on a private jet and a five-star luxury hotel suite in London! We can all go, even Cameron and Dylan!"

"This'll be the best fashion mag ever," exclaimed Yasmin.

"We rock!" yelled Sasha.

"And we're going to rock in London!" whooped Cloe.

©MGA

The plane ride was incredible.

"This trip is going to be so awesome," Cloe said to Cameron. (They would never admit it, but everyone knew that Cloe and Cameron secretly liked each other.) Just then, a handsome British guy stopped at Cloe's seat.

"Excuse me, but I think you're in my seat," he said. Cloe looked up at him and smiled. She was developing a fast crush.

"Oops, I'm sorry," Cloe said. The guy didn't seem too upset.

"Allow me to introduce myself," he said. "I am Nigel Forrester, the 9th Duke of Lessex."

"And I'm Cloe, but my friends call me *Angel*," Cloe said.

"If I may be so bold, it would be an honour to show you Big Ben tomorrow," Nigel said.

"Really? I'd love to!" Cloe answered.

Cameron noticed Cloe talking to Nigel and spent the rest of the plane ride gloomily looking out of the window.

As soon as we hit the city, Sasha pulled out a notebook and started organising everyone's assignments. Cloe and Yasmin would find the ten best places to meet cute guys, Cameron and Dylan would cover sports and entertainment and Sasha and I would check out the London fashion scene. Just then, Cloe got a phone call from Nigel. He wanted to tour the sights with her. I could tell Yasmin was a bit upset that Cloe wouldn't be helping her do the work, but she was too happy for Cloe to say anything about it.

While we were all in the city, scoping out places to write about in our new magazine, Burdine was on a flight with Royale and the Tweevils, on her way to London. She was eating a salad when a cute bulldog named Ozzy came down the aisle. Royale started barking and nipping at the bulldog.

"Will you please control your fat mutt?" Burdine shouted at the owner, a man in a baseball cap.

"Your hairy rat is attacking Ozzy!" replied the man.

"Stuff it," Burdine yelled.

"Come on, Ozzy," said the man. "Let's leave the nasty woman and her mongrel alone."

Things weren't going much better with us girls. Cloe went on her date with Nigel and never showed up to do the story with Yasmin. Yasmin had to do the shoot all on her own. The one good thing was when she found a little lost dog named Ozzy. I went with Sasha to snap pictures, but she hardly let me take any photos at all. By the time we all got back to our hotel room that night, none of us were talking. We have been friends forever, but we have never fought like that before.

"You are the most controlling person I've ever met!" I yelled at Sasha. "You're even worse than Burdine!"

"C'mon guys, chill," said Cloe.

"Like you even know what's been going on, Cloe," Sasha said. "You've been spending so much time with your duke charming that Yasmin's had to cover every hot spot by herself!"

"Yasmin doesn't mind," Cloe said.

"Yes I do!" Yasmin shouted. "You'll be telling us next that you can't make it to the opening of Pinz!"

Cloe got a horrified look on her face. "Oh, no," she said. "I told Nigel I'd go to a dinner party with him."

"Cloe!" Sasha yelled. "The main reason we came to London was to get this scoop for our magazine, right?" Just then, there was a knock on the door. It was Nigel.

"Oh Nigel," Cloe said. "You know my friends are covering the opening of this new rock club for our magazine, right? Can we go after the dinner party?"

Nigel just ignored her question. "Why aren't you dressed?" he asked.

"I *am* dressed," Cloe said.

"You can't be serious," Nigel said. "Surely you have something a little more elegant – like those two lovely girls outside your door.

Sasha got up and ran to the door – and the
Tweevils came flying in. They were
eavesdropping! Cloe walked out with Nigel, and
the Tweevils followed them.
I angrily sat down at the computer and
turned it on. I was completely shocked
when I saw that Sasha had used the
photos I took.
"Sasha," I said, surprised. "You used all of
my pictures!"
"Well yeah," Sasha said. "Yours were
totally better. Friends?"
"Always!" I said.

Roxxi

Sasha, Yasmin and I went shopping, but we
really missed Cloe. She missed us too. Over at Nigel's
dinner party she was feeling sad and alone.
"Nigel," she said, "the Pinz opening starts soon. Can we head out?"
"No!" Nigel said in surprise. "I wouldn't be seen dead at a place like that.
Especially with your misfit friends."
"They are not misfits!" Cloe stammered. "You just don't get them, you royal
jerk."
Cloe ran out and Nigel didn't even try to stop her. The Tweevils had come in and
he was already talking to them. Crying, Cloe set off to run all
the way to Pinz. Just then, Cameron pulled up behind her
on his motorcycle.
"Hey there," he said. "Need a ride somewhere?"
Forcing back her tears, Cloe climbed onto
Cameron's motorcycle and put his spare helmet
on.
"Hold on, Angel," he said. And they zoomed
off into the night.

We were elated when Cloe showed up at the
opening of Pinz later that night.
"Guys," she said, "I haven't been true to myself or to you. I'm so sorry and I
understand if you never want to talk to me again."
"And our resident drama mama is back!" Sasha yelled.
Cloe smiled.
"Friends?" she asked.
"Best friends!" we exclaimed.

63

PINZ NIGHTCLUB LONDON
OPENING SOON

We all jetted off to Pinz with Ozzy.

"Hi, we're from *Your Thing* Magazine," Cloe told the bouncer.

But just then, Burdine appeared. "I demand you have these girls arrested for impersonation!" she yelled. "Call the police now!"

"Guys," Sasha said in a hushed voice. "Don't look now, but we have a major celebrity sighting. It's Byron Powell! The judge from America Rocks!"

As soon as Byron came by, Ozzy jumped into his arms.

"You're his owner?" Yasmin asked.

"Arrest all of them!" Burdine bawled.

"Oh no," said Byron. "It's that absolutely horrific woman from the plane. Come on, girls, follow me."

He turned to the bouncer. "Do *not* let that horrid woman into this club."

We followed Byron into the club as fast as we could. Then he asked us how he could reward us for finding Ozzy.

"Well," said Yasmin. "You could give us an exclusive interview for our new teen magazine."

"How about an exclusive interview plus backstage passes to tomorrow night's Save the Universe Benefit?" he asked.

"Scorchin'!" said Sasha.

We rocked all night. We couldn't believe our luck. Meeting Byron Powell was awesome – but getting an interview and scoring backstage tickets-now, that was just amazing!

SAVE THE UNIVERSE
Your Thing Magazine
7:00pm

But the next day, disaster struck. Our backstage tickets were stolen while we were out of the hotel room! Cloe found a dirty nose bandage on the floor and recognised it as Kaycee's straight away.

"Tweevils!" we yelled.

We had no idea how to get the tickets back.

But then I had an idea.

"Yasmin," I asked. "Did you say that they were only letting rock bands into the club tonight?"

"Yeah," Yasmin said. "So what are we going to do?"

"Well," I said, with a twinkle in my eye. "We could…"

"Kool Kat," said Sasha. "Are you thinking what I'm thinking?"

"Let's become a rock band!" we cried.

We didn't have much time. But we knew we could count on Sasha to get us organised and ready for the night.

"Jade, you're in charge of the wardrobe," Sasha said. "Cloe and Yasmin, you two write the lyrics."

"Wait, what are you going to call yourselves?" Dylan asked.

"How about 'Sasha's Angelz'?" Sasha joked.

"Wait a second, Bunny Boo," said Yasmin. "Angel. Angelz. How about 'Rock Angelz'?"

We ran all over London, getting ready for our big night and practising for our debut as the Bratz Rock Angelz. We found some hip 'n' happening punk outfits to wear and the boys scored us some chic guitars from the local flea market. When we got to the club, Dylan pretended he was the paparazzi, following us around. We ran into the club and started looking for Byron. But when we found him, he didn't look too happy. He was talking to Roxxi, the lead singer from Crash, our favourite band!

"What a night," Byron said. "Roxxi doesn't have any singers. She doesn't have a band and we have an angry mob of people outside! What are we doing to do?"

"Well, *we* can sing," I said...

That night, the Bratz Rock Angelz, plus our new friend Roxxi, rocked like no other band in history. The crowd loved us – and so did Byron! As for Burdine, when she saw us on the stage, she got so angry that she stormed right up there and demanded to have us arrested! The bouncer took her away after that!

That was how the girls with a passion for fashion became the Bratz Rock Angelz. Our song zoomed to the top of the charts and Roxxi became one of our new best friends. And as for the magazine, well – being in London gave us plenty to write about! Cloe wrote a quiz called 'Is your boyfriend a royal jerk?', Sasha wrote about how to form a rock band and Yasmin had an exclusive interview with Byron Powell. I did my very own fashion 'Dos and Don'ts' section. The 'Dos' featured me and my girls in some slamming wear. The 'Don'ts' – well, they featured Burdine and the Tweevils of course!

When you think about it, a lot of this wouldn't have happened without that horrid work experience with Burdine. Sometimes, the best things in life really do come unexpectedly!

©MGA

Designer Diva

Sasha's groovin' gear for a happenin' concert

Headwear

Pink earrings

Long straight hair

Top

Star tank top

Accessories

Bead neclace

Bottom

Denim skirt and leggings

Footwear

Dolly shoes

Yasmin's boho beachwear

Headwear

Fashionable sun glasses

Side pony-tale

Top

cute stripy bikini top

Accessories

toe ring

Belly ring

Bottom

cute Stripy Bikini Bottoms

Spotty Surrong

Footwear

flip flops

THE SHOPS IN THE MALL ARE LACKING INSPIRATION AND WE NEED SOME SERIOUSLY SIZZLIN' STYLES! DESIGN SOME KICKIN' NEW CLOTHES FOR US TO WEAR!

Cloe's glam look for the prom

Headwear

Big Bun

gorgeous earrings

Beautiful crown

Top

glitery corset

Accessories

neclace

Braclet

Bottom

Ball gown

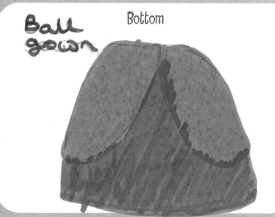

Footwear

high heels

Jade's rockin' outfit for a major party

Headwear

nooped earrings

side fringe long + down

Top

Skull top

Accessories

prikley belt

Bottom

cropped Jeans

Footwear

conease traieners

Fashion Shoot

Cloe

Sasha

Phoebe

Jade

70

Fashion Shoot

Kumi

Dana

Cloe

 oohlala

Glamour Mag

We had such a kickin' time writing articles and taking pics for our fashion-forward magazine – we think you should give it a try too! Grab your best buds and get creative! First you need to get organised like Sasha! Decide who's gonna cover each section of the mag and give everyone assignments.

Fashion - Pick the most ahead-of-the-game gal to write this section. Try any of these ideas to make a stylin' guide to cutting edge fashion!

Fashion Dos and Don'ts

This season's fave colours

How to get the latest look

Makeover magic – pick a friend to do a makeover on and snap each stage with your camera!

Quizzes - No magazine is complete without a few quizzes to tell you the truth about yourself! Here are some quiz ideas to get you started.

Who's your dream date?

What sort of friend are you?

Which Bratz girl would be your best friend?

How do you cope with embarrassing situations?

©MGA

Interviews - Choose an inquisitive friend to go out and snag some exclusive interviews! You could try getting the inside line on.

Your fashion idol

Your crush

A famous actor

Your fave band

How Tos - Get someone organised to write guides to life! They can be about everything and anything – here are some of our fave ideas!

How to Get the Guy

How to Do Your Makeup like a Pro

How to Bust a Bad Mood

How to Be a Super-Slammin' Friend

Now that you've got the words, all you need are the pictures! Get out there with your digital cameras and start snapping. Then put it all together on computer and create the most sizzlin' mag in town!

©MGA

©MGA

©MGA

Stylin' Sportz

Hi, I'm Yasmin and I'm gonna show you that you don't have to be on a school team to get the sportz vibe! It all started when I had an assignment to do for the school magazine, and my girls came along to help me out...

"Come *on!*" bellowed Sasha in my ear. I dropped my notepad and as I bent to pick it up there was a loud collective groan.
"*What?*" I yelled. "What happened?" We were in the gym, watching a basketball match. Our team was looking even more miserable than before.
"Missed!" seethed Sasha. "She had a perfectly good shot and she *missed!*"
I scribbled in my notepad and sighed. We were playing our biggest rivals, and we were being completely beaten.
"What's wrong with them?" groaned Cloe. "Why don't they just *go* for it! They don't seem to have any energy in them! They look so..."
"Fashion backward?" finished Jade. "I don't think I could play well if I had to dress like that!"
We all sighed and nodded. Our sports kits had been the same for years, and this was one time when retro wasn't gonna work – they were definitely from the dark ages of fashion.

I had to write a report on the game for the school magazine, so we stayed and watched the whole defeat. It was embarrassing how badly our team played – and how badly they were dressed. The other team's kit was slammin' – bold colours and off-the-hook designs. Our team wore shapeless skirts and baggy tops in a dreary beige colour. No wonder they were depressed!

We hadn't been to the gym for ages, and as we were filing out after the disastrous game, I noticed a poster that I hadn't seen before. When I read it, I couldn't believe my eyes. Someone had been thinking exactly what we were thinking!

Stylin' Sportz Competition

★ ★ ★ ★ ★ ★ ★

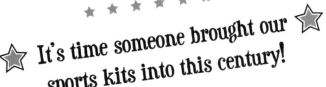 It's time someone brought our sports kits into this century!

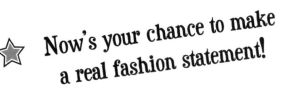 Now's your chance to make a real fashion statement!

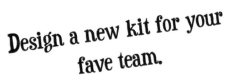 Design a new kit for your fave team.

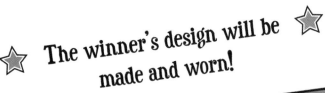 The winner's design will be made and worn!

I called my gals over and showed them the poster.

"Oh wow!" squealed Cloe.

"What a scorchin' idea!" exclaimed Sasha.

"It's fantastic," said Jade.

"Apart from one little thing..."

"What?" we asked.

"*The closing date's tomorrow!*" she cried.

"Oh no – we're gonna have to work really hard to meet that deadline!" groaned Cloe.

"No worries," said Jade coolly – she loves a challenge! "I can come up with loads of designs tonight and we can pick the best one and present it tomorrow – easy!"

"Oh *really?*" said Sasha, folding her arms. "And when did we decide that *you'd* be the one to come up with the design?"

"Chill out, *Bunny Boo*. We all know that I've got the best eye for upcoming fashion trends," Jade replied with a shrug.

"Yes, but we don't want our teams to end up looking weird," I said nervously, thinking of some of Jade's past fashion statements. "Sometimes your style can be a bit out there, *Kool Kat* I mean, they look great on you, but not everyone could pull them off..."

Usually Cloe and I stay out of it when Jade and Sasha go head to head, but this time I had to say something. Jade looked less than thrilled.

"Fine," she said, folding her arms. "If that's how you feel about it."

"I think Jade would do a good job," said Cloe quietly. Jade flashed her a grateful look but Sasha was charging on with her plan.

"We'll do a new kit for the basketball team," she said. "They need the most help."

"Hang on a minute, *Bunny Boo*!" I interrupted.

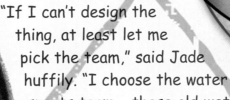

"The football team could use a little fashion aid too, you know."

"If I can't design the thing, at least let me pick the team," said Jade huffily. "I choose the water sports team – those old wetsuits make them look like bits of seaweed."

"I don't mind which team it is – just let's not fight about it!" pleaded Cloe. But we were all too busy trying to get our own way to listen to her.

"This is stupid," I said. "We're never gonna agree on anything with Sasha being bossy and Jade sulking!"

"Hey!" they protested in unison.

"We might as well just work on our own designs," I continued. "At least that way there won't be any arguments."

"Fine by me," said Jade curtly. Sasha nodded.

Cloe looked at us with her big blue eyes open wide.
"I'd rather work together," she said.

"It's only for a day," I replied. "And it'll stop any more rows."

"I suppose..." said Cloe. But she didn't look too convinced.

By the next morning, I wasn't too convinced either! I had worked on designs for hours the night before, but nothing had that spark that makes fashion truly dazzlin'. I was ready to back down and suggest we all work together after all. But when Cloe arrived to pick me up, I could tell that wasn't gonna happen. Jade and Sasha were still being super-stubborn. "How are the designs going?" I asked as I slipped into the back seat next to Jade.

"Awesome," said Sasha. "My kit's lookin' extreme."

"Stylin'," said Jade. "I've had *loads* of ideas." Cloe just rolled her eyes and said nothing. Jade and Sasha were wearing their most stubborn expressions. We drove to school almost in silence. It was horrible, but at least it was only for today!

I decided to forget about the row and just get on with my design. I spent the whole morning doodling instead of paying attention in class, which got me into a bit of trouble with the teachers! But it was no good. I couldn't get the inside track on a single hot idea!

©MGA

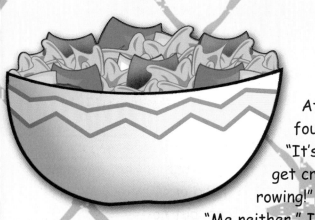

At lunchtime I headed for the canteen and found Cloe drooping miserably over a salad.

"It's no use," she said when she saw me. "I can't get creative when we're all rowing!"

"Me neither," I said, sitting down next to her. "I just can't seem to think of anything really fashion forward!"

"I haven't had a single cutting-edge idea," Cloe added, picking up her drawing pad and waving it at me. "And I've been trying since last night."

"I'm sure we'll think of something eventually," I said, sounding more positive than I felt.

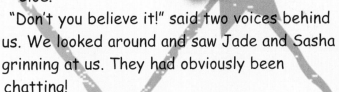

"Jade and Sasha don't seem to be having any problems," said Cloe.

"Don't you believe it!" said two voices behind us. We looked around and saw Jade and Sasha grinning at us. They had obviously been chatting!

"The truth is, we can't concentrate on designing either," Jade admitted.

"It's no fun on your own!"

"So let's put our heads together – we can still do one design for each of us, but this time it'll be a *joint* effort!" said Sasha.

We all cheered up immediately!

We lucked out because we all had a free period that afternoon, so we were able to concentrate on our designs. We pulled out the drawings we had been working on and showed our ideas around. We started commenting on our designs and suddenly everything was back to normal!

"Hey, that's an awesome skirt, *Bunny Boo*," said Jade, looking at Sasha's cheerleading design. "But the top doesn't quite work…"

"How about using the top you designed for the water sports team?" suggested Cloe. "That could look slammin'!"

We tried it out and suddenly the cheerleading design rocked!

We played mix n' match with all our designs and improved them a lot, but we still felt there was something missing.

"Let's go to the gym," I suggested. "It might give us some inspiration – and we can check out all the old kits while we're there!"

We jetted over to the gym and pulled out the various team kits. They were all totally lacking!

"They *so* need our help!" exclaimed Cloe, holding up another shapeless garment with a grin.

Jade pulled out a fresh sheet of paper and took charge of drawing the designs while we brainstormed new creations. As we sorted through the kits the ideas were coming thick and fast, and Jade couldn't draw quickly enough to keep up with us! Soon we had perfected four stylin' designs and we were really excited as we put the old kits away and left the gym.

"Now all we have to do is copy these out onto four sheets, and may the best design win!" smiled Jade.

"Whichever one wins, it'll be a team effort!" Cloe declared.

"Oh no!" exclaimed Sasha, looking at her watch. "There's no time for that! There are only three minutes left until the deadline! Come on!"

We raced through the school to the sports office at top speed, charging through crowds of other students and sprinting like athletes! Jade pushed the paper into the P.E. teacher's hands with thirty seconds to spare. Miss Hurst smiled at us.

"That was close, girls!" she laughed. "Now, whose name should I write on this entry?"

"*All of us*!" we panted, linking arms!

"It is so good to be friends again," said Cloe as she drove us home in her Cadillac. "I hate it when we row!"

"Me too," I agreed. "But we got there in the end – and we couldn't have done it without each other!"

"We should do something to celebrate getting the designs in on time!" said Sasha.

"I'm still feeling super-inspired by all those groovin' sports designs," said Jade. "I bet we could put together some awesome sports-style outfits."

"Let's do it!" I exclaimed. "Let's dress to win and hit the town for a girls' night out!"

Everyone thought that was a scorchin' idea! We zoomed down to the mall for a last-minute outfit hunt, and had loads of fun checking out the sports boutiques we'd never visited before!

Later that evening we met up at Jade's house and coordinated our new team styles. Jade looked awesome in her mini skirt and basketball inspired top. I loved my trackie style jacket and cheerleader skirt, and Cloe's blue outfit was a real head turner! Sasha had picked out the shades she used in her cheerleading outfit. With coordinated lip gloss and eye shadow, we were ready to hit the town!

We went to the Jet Club because Sasha said there was an awesome live band playing. When we arrived, there was a huge crush of people, but as we walked in the dance floor cleared a bit and we saw the boys over by the smoothie bar. We waved to them and they headed our way.

"Ladies!" called Cameron, his face lighting up when he saw Cloe. "What's crackin' with the sports vibe?"

"Oh, we've been exercising our fashion muscles!" Cloe replied with a laugh as she took his arm, "And right now we're in the mood for dancin'! How 'bout you, Blaze?"

Just then the band started cookin' up a cool hip-hop beat and we all dashed onto the dance floor. In our new outfits we were definitely dressed for action. We even persuaded the boys to have a few dances with us!

"I never knew keeping fit could be so much fun!" Jade cried, giggling, as we whirled around the dance floor. We danced all night – only stopping for smoothie refreshment. People kept asking us about our new sporty looks and we had a totally amazing time!

Next day in afternoon assembly, Miss Hurst stood up and we could see she had a single sheet of paper in her hand.

"I am delighted to announce that we have a winner of the Stylin' Sportz Competition!" she said. "There have been some wonderful designs and ideas for all our teams. But the winner obviously gave this a lot of thought and work, and the result is truly exceptional!"

We all looked at each other sadly. She had said 'winner' not 'winners' – that meant it couldn't be us! After all our hard work, we were really bummed. But then she spoke again.

"Even though we asked for just one design," she went on, "this creative entry came up with four fabulous outfits for our four teams – and we simply couldn't choose between them – so we are going to make them all!"

We all held hands in excitement!

"The winner is a team of best friends – Cloe, Sasha, Jade and Yasmin!"

We got to our feet and hugged as everyone clapped and cheered. It felt amazing to have won – but it was even better to share the feeling with my best friends. We could hardly wait to see our outfits in action!

A week later we were at another school basketball match. But this time it couldn't have been more different. Our team looked totally stylin'! We cheered and whistled when they jogged out in their cropped pink tees and blue trousers. They looked ready to win! Then our cheerleading team bounced out, looking scorchin' in their turquoise silky skirts and fitted mini tops. Everyone from school was there to cheer them on. The other team looked totally fashion backward in comparison!

It was a tough game, but our side pushed it to the max and finally won the match with an awesome goal in the last few seconds. But the best part was when they called us down to collect the trophy with the team! "These four girls have boosted my team's morale with their fashion-forward style," announced the team captain. "So they helped win this match!" We raised the trophy with the rest of the team and felt on top of the world!

So you don't have to be sporty to get the sportz vibe! We made our friendship even stronger and had a kickin' cool girls' night out, and it was all thanks to the Stylin' Sportz Competition!

WHETHER YOU'RE A TEAM PLAYER OR A SOLO ARTISTE, HERE ARE SOME TIPS FOR YOUR FAVE SPORT!

jade's

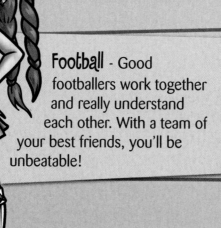

Football - Good footballers work together and really understand each other. With a team of your best friends, you'll be unbeatable!

©MGA

©MGA

Bowling - This is an awesome way to hang out with your best gals! Make your bowling ball unique with your own off-the-hook designs!

Tennis - Doubles, anyone? This is a scorchin' game to play with your best friend – and we dig the chic outfits!

©MGA

Sporty Tips

Golf - This is a relaxing and fun way to keep fit with your friends. Walking is great exercise and you can show off your latest threads on the links!

©MGA

Cheerleading - You need to stay lookin' good while you're performing, so make sure your hair is sleek and shiny and your face is clean and clear.

©MGA

Basketball - Keep your nails short and remove all your jewellery. Make sure your hair is tied back and out of your eyes.

©MGA

Whatever sport you do, have fun and keep yourself lookin' good!

Jade x

How to... Get a

Exercise and playing sports is great for giving your skin a luminous glow, but that's not all you can do! Follow my beauty routine for a glam and flawless look!

The Routine - Every morning and every night, take time to make sure your skin is looking its best.

1. Cleanse

Find a gentle cleanser that suits your skin type.

Pat the cleanser into your face, working up from the chin.

Wash it away and bliss out at how refreshed your skin feels!

2. Tone

A toner removes leftover cleansers and refreshes your face. Apply to your face and allow it to dry. Or a splash of cold water works just as well!

3. Moisturise

Use a moisturiser that contains sun protection, whether the sun is shining or not. This will help to protect your skin.

4. Exfoliate

If your skin looks dull, apply an exfoliating scrub or mask to bring back your naturally glowing complexion. Don't do this more than once a week, though!

Healthy Glow

Tips for Smooth Skin

★ Eat plenty of fresh fruit and vegetables.

★ Avoid tea and coffee.

★ Drink loads of water every day – it's great for your health and fab for your skin!

★ Cut meat and dairy products out of your diet for a few days each month.

★ Don't spend too long in the bath or shower. They can dehydrate your skin.

★ After your bath or shower, pat your skin until it's almost dry and then apply some moisturiser – the moisture will be locked in while your pores are still open.

★ Wear sunscreen – it will protect your delicate face against sun and wind!

★ Sleep – make sure you get enough of it!

★ Invest in some bronzer instead of foundation. A quick sweep across the cheeks will give you that sun-kissed look!

Sun Block 15

Beauty Zone

DO YOU HAVE A PASSION FOR FASHION OR A FEELING FOR FUN? DO THIS QUIZ TO FIND OUT THE BEST MAKEUP PLAN FOR YOU!

When I'm invited to a party the first thing I think is ...
a) where's my makeup bag?
b) who else is going?
c) what shall I wear?
d) who's the DJ?

In my spare time I ...
a) pamper myself.
b) hang out with friends.
c) read fashion mags.
d) listen to my newest CDs.

My best feature is ...
a) whatever I use my makeup skills to highlight!
b) my friendly smile.
c) my body.
d) my dancing feet.

When we hit the shops I head straight for ...
a) the makeup counter.
b) the smoothie bar.
c) the clothes.
d) The CDs.

After a fun night out the first thing I do is ...
a) remove my makeup.
b) plan the next one.
c) hang up my party gear.
d) flip the radio on.

If I could only carry one thing in my bag it would be ...
a) my pocket mirror.
b) my mobile.
c) my credit card.
d) my personal stereo.

The first thing that attracts me to a guy is ...
a) his eyes.
b) his sense of humour.
c) his clothes.
d) his dancing skills.

My friends always ask me to ...
a) give them a makeover.
b) keep their secrets.
c lend them my clothes.
d) make them mixed CDs.

Answers

Mostly A's - Beauty Babe – no one can tell you anything about making the most of your looks! But sometimes you spend so much time on your makeup, you forget about having fun. Try simplifying your look. Push back your hair with a chic clip, slick a thin coating of petroleum jelly on your eyelids and lips, and show the world your natural beauty!

Mostly B's - Social Sweetheart – you're on every guest list and you should go for a look that's fresh, sweet and friendly. Slick on some clear lip gloss, dust some delicate rose blush over your cheeks and highlight your eyes with a brush of chocolate brown mascara. Curl the ends of your hair with tongs to finish your look.

Mostly C's - Funky Fashionista – you've got the lowdown on the hottest new looks, so make sure your makeup is just as hot! Use bold colours and sweep black liner up at the corners of your eyes. Experiment with bright lip gloss and use gel to shape short hair, or go for the tousled look on longer hair.

Mostly D's - Musical Maestro – you know exactly where to find the extreme new sounds – just make sure you have an extreme look to strut to the beat! Tie your hair back in a cute ponytail, use some glitter eyeshadow to dazzle them on the dance floor and go for it!

Blast on the Beach

Hi, I'm *Sasha*, and I'm going to tell you about one very *spooky* party we had last summer!

It was the last day of school and we were all feeling the buzz of a whole summer stretching out in front of us. Everyone wanted to celebrate, but all the ideas were dullsville. Parties at people's houses... bowling... the cinema... it was sounding stale and we needed something a bit different. Then Dylan gave me an idea. He was talking to Cameron as they walked out of school behind us.

"We could go to the beach tomorrow – there are gonna be some blastin' waves," he suggested.

"What did you say?" I asked, whirling around to face him.

"Er, just that the surf's up tomorrow, *Bunny Boo*!" he replied, holding his hands up. "We won't make you ride the waves if you don't want to!"

"No," I laughed. "It's what you said – blastin' on the beach. We should have ourselves a *blastin'* beach party – *tonight*!"

"A midnight party – awesome!" said Nevra.

Everyone thought it was a slammin' idea. We invited loads of our friends and told them to be at the beach at sundown for an off-the-hook party! We chose a beach that was miles away from any houses so we could really crank up the tunes without disturbing anyone.

"I'll bring the music system," said Dylan. "We'll pile our CDs into the car and have ourselves a rockin' night!"

"We'll bring some snacks and refreshments," I added. Eitan remembered that he had some outside lights and promised to bring them to illuminate the groove.

"We'd better get there early so we can set up the music and refreshments," said Yasmin. We agreed to meet the boys on the beach at ten o'clock.

We all piled into Cloe's Cadillac and jetted off to grab some supplies. As we loaded snacks and bottles of water into the car, Jade started grinning.

"Hey gals, this is gonna be a *midnight* picnic party – how much food do we need?"

"There's nothing worse than being hungry at a party!" I said, flashing a grin back at her.

We went home quickly to collect some party threads and then met back at Cloe's house to coordinate our looks.

©MGA

©MGA

I wore my fave
hipster jeans, a
green cami and an
animal-print hat. Jade
chose a purple 'n' pink tunic dress
with a low-slung belt and a hat
angled over one eye. Cloe
looked cute and comfortable in
a sky-blue dress, animal-print
shrug and knee-length suede
boots. Yasmin wore a stylin' sweet
wrapover top with a matching
skirt in 60s psychedelic print and
ankle-length boots. We looked so
fashion fierce that Cloe
did some quick sketches of us in
our stylin' threads!
We all had a change of clothes for
later too – some snugly
gilets and faux-fur
lined boots – it was a
hot summer night but
we were gonna be prepared
if it got chilly!
Soon we were all squeezed into the Cadillac with
piles of food, blankets and changes
of clothes. We picked Nevra
up and headed for the
beach with my latest
hip-hop CD on full
blast. It felt
great to be
cruisin' with my
gals – summer
was here, school
was out and we
were jetting off to a
smoulderin' party!

©MGA

The beach we had chosen was totally remote – we had to drive down a bumpy track to get there. We only passed one house on the way.

"Hey you guys!" said Yasmin. "Look at that cute lil' house over there – how cool would it be to live right by the sea like that?"

"Great for a writer like you, but not for me, *Pretty Princess*!" I laughed. "I like the bright city lights!" We soon turned onto the road that led down to the beach. Cloe parked and patted the dash.

"Sorry about that," she said to the Cadillac. "I know you hate bumpy roads."

"Talkin' to your wheels is the first sign of madness, girl!" I teased her as we hopped out and started to unpack.

We piled all the things we had brought into our arms and jetted down to the shore. That beach is one of our fave hot spots – the sea is crystal clear, the sand is fine and we always have it to ourselves! Behind the beach is a shady little wood, which is ideal in the daytime when the sun gets too scorchin'. But we had never been there at night before!

We laid out the food on the blankets and filled some buckets with ice to keep the water chilled. Then Jade's mobile rang. She flipped it onto speakerphone – it was Dylan.

"Hi Fox, what's happenin'?" asked Jade. "Got the music sorted?"

"Yeah, almost. We've hit a delay though – we have to wait to pick up the speakers. So we'll be a bit late – but we'll see ya'll before midnight."

"No worries—" began Jade, but I cut in. I really hate it when plans go wrong! "Fox, isn't there anything you can do?" I asked. "We planned all the timing for this and now we're just gonna be sitting here with nothing to do."

"Sorry, *Bunny Boo*, can't help it," replied Dylan. "We'll see you when we get there."

He rang off and I frowned. Cloe looked at me and giggled, which annoyed me.

"Chill out, girl!" she said casually.

"What are we supposed to do while we wait?" I asked. "We haven't even got any music."

"How about another kind of entertainment?" suggested Yasmin. "I'll tell you a story to pass the time." Yasmin is a totally talented storyteller! We all agreed eagerly.

We sat down in a circle by the shore as the sun finally set and the stars started to twinkle. Yasmin began to speak in a hushed voice.
"We've never been to this beach at night before," she said, "so you guys have never heard why it's always deserted. By day it's a slammin' venue for sun worshippers like Sasha..." she grinned at me... "but by night it's the realm of the *black wolf*."

Yasmin paused. All we could hear was the gurgle of the waves on the shore and the distant whisper of the wind in the trees.

"They say that it only comes out when there's a full moon," continued Yasmin. I saw Cloe look up at the full moon and give a little shiver. "On the moonlit beach it stalks its prey. The black wolf has flaming red eyes and long, sharp, yellowing teeth. Only one person has ever seen it and lived to tell the grisly tale..."

That was when we heard it. A long, drawn-out howl from the wood behind the beach! Yasmin's story had got us pretty tense, and we froze in horror. Then the howl came again, even louder than before!

97

Cloe, ever the drama queen, gave a piercing scream.

"It's the black wolf! It's gonna eat us! We've gotta get outta here!" She clutched me.

"Get *off*!" I yelled. "That hurt! You're totally overreacting, Cloe – calm down!"

"Calm down? Have you flipped? There's a *black wolf* out there!"

Yasmin was trying to say something, but we were all yelling too loudly to hear her.

"There's definitely *something* out there," said Jade, and her voice trembled slightly. I was nervous too, which made me even edgier. *Angel* was on the verge of hysterics.

"Of course there isn't a black wolf out there!" Nevra squeaked. "But what if there's *something* worse?"

"Like what?" I shouted over Cloe's wails.

"It could be *anything*!" yelled Nevra, who was getting almost as bad as Cloe. "What if it's something that only comes out at night and—"

"Oh don't be *ridiculous*!" I moaned.

"Quiet!" Jade demanded suddenly. *Kool Kat* hardly ever raises her voice and we all stopped shouting and stared at her. She had gone very pale.

"Where's Yasmin?" she asked.

We all looked around in horror. Where Yasmin had been sitting there was just an empty space!

©MGA

"It's the black wolf!" screamed Cloe. "It's taken Yasmin!"

"It's a wild animal!" wailed Nevra.

"Shut up, both of you!" I snapped, totally losing my temper and feeling kinda close to screaming myself. "Call her name! Yasmin!"

"Yasmin!" we all shouted. To our relief we heard her voice answering us.

"Over here!" It was coming from the wood. Jade and I raced over there, with Cloe and Nevra shivering behind us. Yasmin was sitting on the ground in the wood next to a tiny black-and-white puppy. One of its paws was cut and bloodied, and as we ran up it lifted its head and gave another mournful howl.

"A puppy!" I said, turning to Cloe. "See? Why do you always have to be such a drama queen?"

"Why did you just go off like that?" Nevra asked Yasmin crossly. "You really scared us!"

"I tried to tell you that it sounded like an animal in pain," said Yasmin calmly. "But you were all yelling so loudly you didn't hear me."

"If Cloe and Nevra had stayed calm we wouldn't have *been* yelling," I said. "For someone who says she wasn't scared, you went pretty pale yourself," snapped Cloe. We were all totally freakin' out.

©MGA

"Oh stop it," said Yasmin impatiently. "This puppy can't walk. Let's drive it down to that house we passed and ask if they can help."

We took one of the blankets and gently lifted the whimpering puppy onto it. Then four of us took the corners and lifted it up, while Cloe went ahead to start the car. We were all starting to chill out – until Cloe turned the key in the ignition and nothing happened.

"Ooohhh nooo," wailed Cloe. "We're stuck here! This place is *haunted*, I can *feel* it! What have the spooks done to my car?"

I walked around to the front of the Cadillac and put my hands on my hips.

"You left your lights on – the battery's gone dead. Way to go, Cloe."

"We'll just have to walk," said Yasmin firmly.

"Walk?" squeaked Nevra. "All the way down that dark track?" added Cloe in a horrified tone.

©MGA

I didn't want to do it either, but I wasn't in any mood to agree with Cloe.

"Stay here then," I shrugged. "I'm sure we can carry one little puppy without your help."

"You can't leave us here!" cried Nevra.

"One day something will scare *you* and then *you'll* know what it feels like!" said Cloe as we started the long walk down the uneven track. Yasmin and Jade were carrying the front of the blanket and concentrating on leading the way. Nevra and I had the back two corners and Cloe was walking along next to us, muttering about spooks and black wolves.

"Enough already!" I snapped at her.

"You are always overreacting, Cloe!"

"Just because you don't have any imagination!" she retorted.

"I wish I'd never started the silly story," sighed Yasmin.

"So do I," I said.

"Don't blame Yasmin!" said Cloe hotly.

It was so dark that even in the moonlight we could hardly see where we were going. Suddenly there was a loud bump and Cloe gave a scream. I rolled my eyes.

"What now?"

"I tripped over and – ow! I think I've sprained my ankle!" wailed Angel.

We put the blanket down and the puppy started to howl again as we went over to help Cloe. We pulled her to her feet, but she couldn't walk.

"Perfect," I said, still feeling cross. "Now we've got two of you to carry!"

Yasmin and Jade took the puppy between them and Nevra and I supported Cloe, who limped along between us, groaning at every step. The puppy kept howling and all of a sudden I saw the funny side of it! I started shaking with laughter and Cloe looked at me in amazement.

"What's up, *Bunny Boo*?"

"All we need now is the black wolf to come after us and it would be the perfect night!" I spluttered, wiping tears of laughter out of my eyes. Cloe stared at me for a few seconds, then started to giggle too.

"I guess I got a bit freaked!" she admitted. "I'm sorry, *Bunny Boo*."

"I'm sorry too – I love you exactly the way you are, *Angel*!

We stopped and hugged, still giggling, while Yasmin and Jade paused and sighed.

"Now we've got that sorted out, do you think we could keep moving?" asked Jade. But I could tell from her voice that she was grinning!

We stumbled on down the track until we saw the little white house ahead of us. All the lights were on and the front door was wide open. As we walked closer we saw two figures in the garden.

"Benjy!" called a man's voice. "Here boy!"

The puppy began to whimper and we realised that he must live here. We hurried up the garden path.

"Excuse me!" called Yasmin. "Is this your dog?"
The man rushed up to us with a woman close behind him.
"We found him in the wood with a cut paw," explained Jade.
"Oh thank you!" gasped the woman. "We've been so worried!"

They invited us inside, but just then we heard a car coming down the track – it was the boys! Jade ran out to stop them.

We said goodbye to Benjy and his owners and piled into the car – it was a tight squeeze with the boys and all their music equipment! As we drove back down to the beach we told the boys about Yasmin's story and about finding the puppy.

When we got back to the beach we helped the boys set up the music system and got ready to party. Poor Cloe couldn't do any dancing, but she seemed happy to sit on a blanket beside Cameron. We had a blastin' late-night party and so many guests turned up that the beach was jumpin' with our dancin' feet!

We partied until the pink sunrise lit up the sky. As our guests started to leave and we began to clear up, we were all yawning loudly!
"Shall I tell a story to keep us awake?" suggested Yasmin with a cheeky smile.
"NO!" we all yelled together!

©MGA

Yasmin's Creative

I LOVE TELLING STORIES AND USING WORDS TO MAKE PEOPLE HAPPY OR SAD – OR SCARED! IF YOU WANT TO BE A WRITER, HERE ARE MY TIPS TO GET YOU STARTED ON YOUR FIRST STORY.

Good Writers Love Reading

Here are some different kinds of stories.
Circle the three that you like best!

Thriller	Horror
Romance	Adventure
Mystery	Western
Action	Sports
Animal	Sad
Funny	School
Fantasy	Family
Science Fiction	Friendship

Write a Story

1. Theme

What kind of story are you going to write? Have a look at the different kinds of stories listed above. Which three did you circle? Pick one of those and think about what is going to happen in your story.

My theme is going to be

....

Writing Tips

2. Character

Now it's time to create your first character! Your characters can be anyone or anything you like. To get you started, fill out this short profile of your character.

My character's name is...Jessica...........................

My character is...16...................years old.

My character lives in......St. Albans................

My character lives with .....mum, dad, sister......

My character likes......chocolate...............

My character hates.......shrimp......................

My character's best friend is.......Sam.......................

My character is crushing on.......Cameron...............

You can copy out this list and use it to create as many characters as you want!

3. Setting

Where are you going to set your story? You could write about something that happens at school, on holiday or at home. Set your story in outer space or under the sea! Let your imagination go wild!

My story will be set in......a house......

4. Starting your Story

You're almost ready to start writing! You've created your first character. You've decided what kind of story it's going to be and you know where it's going to be set. Now all you need is something to write on! Find a really groovin' notebook, or decorate one yourself. Now grab a pen and get creative!

Top Tips

Read as much and as often as you can.

Write at least 50 words every day. Practice makes perfect!

Write from your own experiences.

When you have written a chapter, don't look at it for a day. Then go back and re-read it. You'll find lots of ways to make it sound even better!

Most of all, have fun! If you enjoy what you're writing, other people will enjoy reading it. Good luck!

Yasmin X

Winter Beauty

Hair - You've gotta look after your crowning glory!

Once a week, use a deep conditioning treatment after your usual shampoo.

If you blow dry your hair, use the lowest setting on the hairdryer.

The wet and windy weather can really damage your hair. Wear a stylin' hat to protect your locks!

Skin - Your skin can be damaged by the cold weather. Make sure you follow a careful cleansing routine every night and morning.

Cleanse – use a light and gentle cleanser to clear your pores.

Tone – toner removes leftover cleanser and refreshes your face.

Moisturise – a Vitamin E lotion will help avoid pimples.

Eyes - The eye area is super-delicate, so use a special eye cream in the morning and at night to protect your peepers.

Keep a pair of sunglasses in your bag to protect your eyes from wind and bright sun rays.

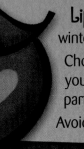

Lips - Your lips can become chapped in the winter if you don't keep them well moisturised.

Choose a tinted lip balm instead of gloss to keep your lips plumped and perfect for all those holiday parties!

Avoid licking your lips.

A CAREFUL BEAUTY REGIME IS IMPORTANT ALL YEAR ROUND, BUT AS IT GETS COLDER YOU NEED A BIT OF EXTRA LOVIN' CARE! FOLLOW OUR FAVE TIPS FOR A TOTALLY FUNKALISH WINTER LOOK – TIP TO TOE!

Hands - Everyone sees your hands, so make sure they look soft and supple this winter!

Milk is fabulous for softening skin. Fill the sink with warm water, add a tablespoon of milk and your fave aromatherapy oil and let your hands soak for five minutes. Then take them out, pat dry and moisturise.

Always wear gloves outside.

Nails - Now that your hands are looking great, don't forget about your nails! Follow these tips for eye-catching fingertips.

Massage petroleum jelly into your cuticles every night.

Every few days, brush your nails with cuticle oil or petroleum jelly.

File your nails to keep them in shape.

Legs - Don't forget about your pins, just because they're covered up in winter gear! The skin on your legs is just as important as everywhere else.

After every bath or shower, leave your legs a little bit damp and slap on the moisturiser. Your legs will love you!

Feet - Killer heels, glam boots and strappy sandals – we make our feet work hard! Be sweet to your feet this winter.

To keep your feet soft and supple, use a pumice stone to exfoliate in the bath.

Rub a moisturising lotion into them every night.

Use a lotion that contains petroleum or glycerin for extra softening power!

Midnight Party Picnic

Here are some of our fave ideas and recipes for a slammin' midnight picnic. You could hold one in the back garden and turn an ordinary slumber party into an unforgettable night under the stars!

Get Planning

How many tents will you need?

Take plenty of rugs, cushions and blankets to snuggle up in under the stars.

There's nothing better than flasks of hot chocolate as you sit by the campfire!

Hand out lucky dip bowls filled with crisps, popcorn and sweets!

Make sure everyone brings stylin' and cosy campfire wear. Snuggly gilets and faux-fur lined boots will keep you warm and funky.

Ask everyone to bring something to eat and something to do.

Remember to take a torch for those spooky ghost stories …

Make sure you'll have music – take a battery-powered stereo and plenty of jumpin' tunes.

Banana Surprise

You will need:
1 banana for each person
Chocolate buttons
Foil

1. Slice each banana length-wise but not all the way through.
2. Fill the crack with chocolate buttons and squeeze the banana together gently.
3. Wrap each banana in foil and cook them over the campfire until all the chocolate has melted. Divine!

Melting Marshmallows

You will need:
Marshmallows
A toasting fork

1. Put a marshmallow on the end of the toasting fork and hold it above the campfire for a few seconds.
2. Eat!

Yearbook Photos

Spring Term

Jade always starts the year with a fashion sensation!

Summer Term

Cloe experimented with cowboy chic!

Autumn Term

Yasmin strutted casual-cool style for back-to-school

Winter Term

Sasha bundled up in cozy, outdoorsy gear.